Collins

Easy Learning

English

Age 9-10

My name is ....

I am .... years old.

I go to .... School.

My favourite book is ....

Anne Loadman

How to use this book

- Find a quiet, comfortable place to work, away from other distractions.
- Tackle one topic at a time.
- Help with reading the instructions where necessary, and ensure that your child understands what to do.
- Help and encourage your child to check their own answers as they complete each activity.
- Discuss with your child what they have learnt.
- Let your child return to their favourite pages once they have been completed, to talk about the activities.
- Reward your child with plenty of praise and encouragement.

Special features

- Parent's notes: These are divided into 'What you need to know', which explain the key English idea, and 'Taking it further', which suggest activities and encourage discussion with your child about what they have learnt. The words in bold are key words that you should focus on when talking to your child.

Published by Collins
An imprint of HarperCollins*Publishers*
77–85 Fulham Palace Road
Hammersmith
London
W6 8JB

Browse the complete Collins catalogue at
www.collins.co.uk

First published in 2006
© HarperCollins*Publishers* 2008

10 9 8 7 6

ISBN-13 978-0-00-730109-6

The author asserts the moral right to be identified as the author of this work.

All rights reserved. No part of this publication may be reproduced, stored in a retrieval system, or transmitted in any form or by any means, electronic, mechanical, photocopying, recording or otherwise, without the prior written permission of the Publisher or a licence permitting restricted copying in the United Kingdom issued by the Copyright Licensing Agency Ltd., 90 Tottenham Court Road, London W1T 4LP.

British Library Cataloguing in Publication Data
A Catalogue record for this publication is available from the British Library
Written by Anne Loadman

Design and layout by Lodestone Publishing Limited, Uckfield, East Sussex; www.lodestonepublishing.com
Illustrated by Rachel Annie Bridgen;
www.shootingthelight.com
Edited by Jean Rustean
Cover design by Susi Martin
Cover illustration by John Haslam
Printed and bound in China

Acknowledgements
The Publishers would like to thank the following for permission to reproduce the texts and extracts in this book:
'A Poem to Be Spoken Silently…' © Pie Corbett, reprinted by permission of the author.
Flapjacks recipe courtesy of Sainsbury's.

Contents

Prefixes

Auto- means self

- Write auto- in front of these words to make new words.

    _____biography   _____

    _____graph   _____

    _____mobile   _____

    _____matic   _____

- Now cover each word and try to spell it correctly.
- Can you find any more auto- words?

Bi- means two or both

- Match the bi- word to its meaning.

    A two wheeled vehicle   binoculars

    Helps you to see things at a distance   bilingual

    Something that happens every two years   bicycle

    An aeroplane with two sets of wings   biennial

    Able to speak two languages   biplane

- Now cover each bi- word and write it out below.

    _____

    _____

    _____

    _____

    _____

What you need to know   How to use and spell words with the prefixes **auto-**, **bi-**, **trans-** and **tele-**.
A prefix is a group of letters that can be added to the beginning of a word to change its meaning.

Trans- means across or through

• Find the best trans- word to fit in each sentence.

translucent   transfer   transplant   transform   transport

The footballer was on the _____ list.

My favourite form of _____ is the train.

This thin paper is _____.

I am going to _____ this old box with paint and stencils.

He was lucky to have had a kidney _____ .

Tele- means at a distance

• Choose the correct tele- words to match the definitions.

telepathy   television   telescope   teleport   telephone

_____ – something to look through

_____ – something to watch

_____ – Dr Who can do this in his TARDIS

_____ – you can talk to your friends on this

_____ – the ability to know what someone is thinking

Taking it further Collect words using the prefixes on these pages. Look at newspapers, magazines, advertisements and signs and make lists of words you find.

Root words

Hidden roots

**Root words are the smaller words from which longer words are made.
Sign is a root word, from which signal, signify and signpost, can be made.**

- Put a circle around the root word inside these longer words. The first one has been done for you.

dis(**appear**)ance

signature

reviewed

helpfulness

selection

untruthful

More root words

- How many words can you find that include the following root words? (Hint: try adding different prefixes and suffixes.)

employ _____

fire _____

foot _____

line _____

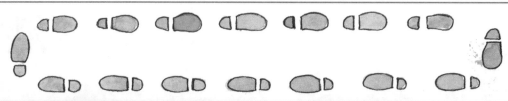

What you need to know Many long words are made from a shorter root word. The spelling of the root word does not usually change when it is part of a longer word. You can build up words by adding prefixes and suffixes to root words.

Follow the pattern

Knowing the root word can help you to spell longer words.

- Follow the pattern and spell the words.

permit	permission	permitted
admit		
commit		
submit		
omit		
emit		

Jolly Joke

Why did the thief wear blue gloves?

Because he didn't want to be caught red-handed!

Experiment with root words

- The root word 'hand' can be part of many other words:

  handy   handful   underhand   handle
  handling   handkerchief   handbag   freehand

- How many more can you find?

Taking it further   Write some prefixes and suffixes on small pieces of card or paper. Then write a list of root words. Add the prefixes and suffixes to either side of the root words and see which new words you can make.

Words from other countries

In a dictionary, after the word listing, there will be a word or some letters in brackets e.g. (Gr) Greek or (Ind) Indian, telling you where the word comes from.

Words from Italy

Many Italian words we use are to do with food:

macaroni   lasagne   spaghetti   pizza

Other Italian words you may know are:

piano   umbrella   graffiti   motto

- Look at their spelling patterns, like the gn in lasagne.
- Cover each Italian word and write it out below.

_____ _____ _____ _____

_____ _____ _____ _____

Words from India

In Victorian times, India was part of the British Empire.
Here are some words with different spelling patterns for you to learn:

di**ngh**y   **pyj**amas   jo**dhp**urs

- Practise spelling these words below.

_____ _____ _____

Words from France

We use some French words in our everyday lives:

boutique   café   metre   centimetre

- Can you think of any more? Write them here.

_____ _____ _____

_____ _____ _____

What you need to know The English language is constantly changing and we borrow words from many countries. Knowing where words come from can help us to spell them if we become aware of their spelling patterns.

Word meanings

in-struc-tion
mal-func-tion

- Use a dictionary or the Internet to look up the following words to find their meanings and find out which country they came from.

Word	Meaning	Where it came from
bungalow		
restaurant		
kayak		
robot		
anorak		

How do trees get on the Internet?

They have to log in!

New words

Here are some words which are quite recent additions to our language. Many of them come from new inventions.

skateboard   Internet   iPod   yuppie

bouncebackability   microwave

- Find out their meanings if you are not sure.
- Can you find any more?

Taking it further   Look out for words from other countries when you are shopping. Many shops and supermarkets have goods from other countries. Read the name of the product and try and guess where it came from. How many foreign words can you find on objects in your own house?

Unstressed vowels

-able or -ible?

In some words, the vowel sound is not very clear, or even missed out. These sounds are called unstressed vowels.

Words that end with -able or -ible can sound very similar.

- Add -able or -ible onto the following word starts.

  port _____   horr_____   like_____

  respons_____   wash_____   terr_____

- Check them by looking them up in a dictionary.
- The following words end in -ible. Can you think of any rules to work out which words are likely to end this way?

  sensible   divisible   gullible   incredible

What is missing?

A vowel sound has been missed out of the following words.
- Put the correct vowel into the words.

  int__rest   c__mpany   carp__t

  freed__m   pois__nous   diff__rent

  manag__r   d__scribe   fact__ry

- Can you think of any more? Make a list and practise spelling them.

What you need to know   Some longer words have vowel sounds that are not clear when we say them.
Children need to be aware of these sounds as they are often missed out in spellings, or the wrong vowel is used.

Changing words

Verbs to nouns

We can change some verbs into nouns by adding a suffix.

- Find which suffixes will make sense in the following words.
  Some verbs will need to change before adding the suffix.

Verb	-ist	-ism	-ology
hypnotise			
tour			
cycle			
escape			

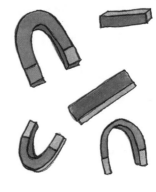

Jolly Joke

Why did the witch need help with her homework?

Because she was having trouble spelling!

Nouns to verbs

Nouns can be changed into verbs by adding the suffixes:
  -ise   -ify   -en

- Which suffixes can make verbs out of these nouns?
  Some nouns will need to change before adding the suffix.
  (Hint: try saying the words out loud with each ending.)

Noun	-ise	-ify	-en
terror			
magnet			
vandal			
length			
fright			
material			
horror			
light			

Taking it further   Play the changing words game on a journey. One person picks a suffix and the other person has to find a word to fit it. Other suffixes you could use are: **-ed**, **-ing** and **-er**. How many words can you find for each?

Word order

Sentence order

Look at this sentence.

Every day, at half past two, Gill went to the café, next to the church, for a cup of coffee.

It could be written:

Gill went to the café, next to the church, every day, for a cup of coffee, at half past two.

- Find at least two more ways of writing out the same sentence so that it still makes sense.

_____

_____

_____

_____

Changing order

- Choose some of the following phrases and add them to the sentence starts below. Put a comma between each phrase and a full stop at the end of each sentence.

who had just got off the bus   tired and panting   lay on the steps

whose bag was heavy   stopped at the corner   stumbled up the hill

waiting for his dinner   for a rest   through the snow

Abdul, _____

_____

The old dog, _____

_____

The old lady, _____

_____

- Can you find other ways to put the phrases together to make sentences?
- Which order do you like best?

Most important words

You need to know which words in a sentence are the most important and must be left in. Look at the sentence below. The important words are underlined.

<u>Billy Roberts</u>, the new <u>captain of Newtown Rovers</u> football team, was talking in the <u>local newspaper</u>, about the thrilling <u>match</u> on <u>Tuesday</u>, when his team <u>won 4–0</u>, in an exciting game against <u>City</u>.

Take the important words and use them to make a shorter sentence, like this:

Billy Roberts, Newtown Rovers' captain, talked in the local newspaper about Tuesday's match against City, which Rovers won 4–0.

- Now make your own version of this sentence by changing the word order.

_____

_____

_____

Which words can be left out?

- Cross out the unnecessary words in each of the following sentences.
- Then write out the important words in a new, shorter sentence below.

Tall Steven Sutherland, who was 24 in a month's time, had returned from a lovely, long holiday in Australia, where he had stayed for the last six months.

_____

_____

_____

The guitarist, whose favourite food was broccoli, was playing at his first outdoor concert, even though it was raining, and broke his string in the middle of the first song.

_____

_____

_____

Taking it further   Take a short newspaper article and set yourself a target number of words, e.g. 100. Underline or highlight the most important information and rewrite the article in the target number of words or less.

Clauses

Main clauses

A main clause is part of a sentence that contains a subject and a verb.

- Underline the main clause in the following sentences. The first one has been done for you.

The girl fell after slipping on a stone.

In the dark, an owl hooted.

The teacher was pleased because the class were listening.

Out in the garden the gnome sat by the pond.

Steven cheered as his team scored a goal.

Subordinate clauses

As well as the main clause, there will be one or more subordinate clauses, which give us extra information.

- Circle the subordinate clauses in these sentences. The first one has been done for you.

Abbi was feeling unwell, as she had eaten too much.

Although it was night-time, the street was full of people.

The dog barked when he saw his owner.

The silver spaceship landed somewhere in the woods.

Up above them, a rainbow arched across the sky.

What you need to know   What a main clause is and how to recognise it. How to use clauses to combine shorter sentences to make a longer one.

Shorter sentences can be joined together by rewriting them in clauses and using joining words.

e.g.   The boy was pleased. He scored a goal. His team played well.
The boy was pleased because he scored a goal and his team played well.

- Combine the following sentences.

The frog croaked. The rain fell. The pond became full.

_____

_____

The sun shone. The class were happy. They could play rounders.

_____

_____

Josh likes playing tennis. It is his favourite sport. He is a good player.

_____

_____

The boy tripped. He fell over. He lost his ice cream.

_____

_____

Jolly Joke

What happened to the frog's car when it broke down?

It got toad away!

Building up longer sentences

- Add two subordinate clauses to the main clauses below to make longer sentences. The main clause can be anywhere in a sentence.

e.g.   The lion roared, because far in the distance, he saw fire.

The goalkeeper dived, _____ ,

_____ .

_____ , a small cottage could be seen,

_____ .

_____ , _____ ,

a sports car was parked.

Taking it further   Write some main clauses and subordinate clauses on pieces of card. Shuffle and place them in two piles. Take one card from each pile and see if your sentence makes sense. You could have two piles of subordinate clauses to extend this activity.

Connectives

Connectives are words that join sentences, or parts of sentences, together. Connectives can be small words like 'and' or 'but' or longer words like 'however' and 'although'.

- Here are some sentence parts. Choose **and**, **but** or **so** to join the parts together to make complete sentences.

  Our school netball team tries hard _____ we hardly ever win.

  I would like to come _____ my mum won't let me.

  We wanted to win the football match _____ we had to work as a team.

  My boots are muddy _____ I will take them off before I make a mess.

  I want to have pizza for tea _____ ice cream for supper.

More connectives

- Join the pairs of sentences with a connective from below to make one, longer sentence.

  because   even though   although   as

  Jack went up the hill. He was very tired.

  _____

  Michael Owen scored. The other team were playing well.

  _____

  The monkey looked bored. He wanted to live in the wild.

  _____

  I had to share my cake. My brother didn't have one.

  _____

What you need to know Sentences and parts of sentences can be joined by connectives. They can be single words like **and**, **but** and **so**, or phrases like **after a few moments** or **even though**. Connectives help writing to flow and make it interesting.

Spot the connectives!

- Underline the connectives in the following passage.

  Remember, connectives can be phrases as well as single words and can start a sentence.

Bradley wanted to be a footballer, although he knew it would be difficult. In spite of the training, and the early nights, he knew it would be worth it. However, there were a few problems to be overcome. Firstly, he had to get over his injury, because he had hurt his ankle in a cup match. Then he had to get a trial with his local team, although he had read in the paper that they were looking for new players. Finally, there was his own lack of confidence. He had to believe in himself.

Jolly Joke

When is a car not a car?
When it turns into a garage!

Better than 'then'

'Then' is a connective of time but it is often overused.

- Add the connectives to the following passage to make it interesting.

  At last   A few moments later   Before   Without waiting

Peter was sitting at his computer, playing a racing game. _____ he could say anything, one of the cars drove out of the computer screen. Peter couldn't believe his eyes. _____ another car followed it. _____ Peter tried to catch the cars as they raced around his bedroom. _____ he managed to trap one and pick it up. To his surprise, the driver spoke to him!

Taking it further   Play the connectives game: make up a story by taking turns to think of sentences. Try to use a different connective to start each sentence.

Standard English

Agreement of verbs

It is important to be able to write correct or 'Standard' English.

- The verbs in these sentences aren't quite right. Read the sentences and write them out correctly.

We <u>was given</u> one each.

_____

I <u>drawed</u> a wonderful picture of a horse.

_____

They <u>was</u> happy to be on holiday.

_____

You <u>gived</u> me my present before my birthday.

_____

Agreement of tenses

- This article should be in the past tense (it happened in the past) but the writer has made some mistakes and used some present tense verbs.
- Underline each incorrect verb and write the correct one above it.

I was walking down Beverley Road and my friend,

Barry, comes up to me and says, "I've lost my dog, Buster."

"I'll help you look for him," I says.

We walked down Olive Gardens and he says, "I bet he's

gone under the fence into the cricket ground!"

We looked through a gap in the fence and there he is, digging up the grass!

I could see a red-faced man who runs up to Buster, waving his arms and shouting.

Buster sees him and got a shock. He tries to squeeze under the fence, but he gets

stuck. Barry was starting to panic, but Buster just got through in time!

What you need to know There is a difference between the way we speak to friends and family and the way we write. When we write, we need to use Standard English, so that everyone can understand us.

Double negatives

In a sentence, two negative words cancel out each other.
e.g. I **haven't** done **nothing** should be: I **haven't** done **anything**.

- Rewrite the following sentences correctly.

We didn't go nowhere.

_____

He didn't talk to no-one.

_____

She hadn't not done her homework.

_____

I didn't say nothing.

_____

Jolly Joke

What kind of garden does a baker have?

A flour garden!

Putting it all together

- Read this short paragraph and rewrite it in Standard English.

Me and me friend Judith were on our way to the park, when she says she's lost her money. We looked everywhere, but we couldn't find it. We went on the swings and walked by the duck pond. Judith was right upset and I tries to cheer her up by telling her a joke. We wasn't having a good time, until Judith remembers that she give her money to her mum this morning!

_____

_____

_____

_____

_____

_____

Taking it further Get into the habit of checking your writing. Make sure that you keep the tenses the same and that you use the right kinds of verbs.

Acronyms

Making acronyms

Acronyms are words made up from the beginning letters of the words contained in it, e.g. CD stands for compact disc.

- Find the acronyms in the following phrases.

Phrase	Acronym
Please turn over	
British Broadcasting Corporation	
Royal Automobile Club	
Amateur Athletics Association	
Do-it-yourself	

Common acronyms

- Here are some common acronyms. Look up their meanings in a dictionary and write out the words that make up the acronym.

radar

_____

NASA

_____

RAF

_____

asap

_____

scuba

_____

What you need to know Some everyday words have been made from longer words by missing out letters and putting in an apostrophe, or by taking off part of the word.

Omissions

Taking away parts of words

An omnibus is usually known as a bus. The prefix omni-, meaning all, has been missed out.

- Take away parts of the following words to make shorter, everyday words.

  telephone _____

  aeroplane _____

  television _____

  submarine _____

Jolly Joke

Where do TVs go for a holiday?

Anywhere remote!

Missing letters

**When we say it is something 'o'clock', this is a short way of saying 'of the clock'. Some letters have been missed out.
We put an apostrophe in place of the missing letters in a phrase and a full stop when a single word has been shortened.**

- Here are some words and phrases which have been shortened.
  Write out the words in full.

  don't _____

  Prof. _____

  can't _____

  Rev. _____

- How many more can you find?

Taking it further   Make up some acronyms of your own e.g. AHM – automatic homework machine!
Look for examples of acronyms in newspaper articles or reading books. Make a list.

Legends

Legends are tales about heroes or heroines who mainly lived long ago. They were usually very brave, clever or strong.

Here is a Cornish legend about Jack the Giant Killer.

Jack was a farmer's son who lived near Land's End in the time of King Arthur. The people were being terrorised by a giant called Cormoran, who stole the villagers' cattle. The lord of the manor called a public meeting in the village square and offered a reward for anyone who could slay the fearsome giant.

The young boy Jack was the only one who took up the challenge. Everyone laughed because Jack was so small and so young.

Undeterred, Jack had a plan. He dug a huge pit near the giant's home on St. Michael's Mount and disguised its opening with twigs and straw. Jack waited till nightfall then blew his horn, as loudly as he could. The angry giant came running out and fell into the pit, where he died.

Everyone celebrated and Jack was given a sword, and a belt embroidered with the words 'Jack the Giant Killer'.

- Now answer these questions.

- What qualities do you think Jack had that made him a hero?

  _____

- What clues are there to let you know that this story is from a long time ago?

  _____

  _____

  _____

- Look up and write down the meanings of the following words.

  manor _____

  undeterred _____

  nightfall _____

What you need to know The features that are often found in legends, myths and fables.
Children should be able to work out the message or moral in a story and know how to answer comprehension-style questions.

Fables

Jolly Joke

Why did the fox cross the road?
To get the chicken!

Stories with a moral

Fables are stories that have a message, called a 'moral', hidden in the story, e.g. pride comes before a fall. Fables often have animals as the main characters.

One famous author of fables was a Greek called Aesop.
Here is a version of his fable 'The Fox and the Crow'.

There was once a very hungry fox, who saw a black crow with a huge piece of cheese in his beak.

"Will you share your cheese with me, my friend?" asked the fox. The crow didn't answer, but took his cheese and flew up to a high branch of a nearby tree.

The fox was so hungry and the cheese looked so tasty that the fox thought of a cunning plan.

"Oh brother crow, how handsome you look up there," he said. The crow was pleased with this compliment.

The fox continued, "And I have heard that you have the most beautiful voice in the forest. Please sing for me."

The crow was swollen with pride and opened his beak to sing. He let out a terrible croak. As he did so, the cheese fell from his beak and the fox greedily snatched it away and ate it up.

The crow was left with nothing.

- Can you work out the moral of this fable? Write it down here.

_____

_____

- Try to write your own fable that has the moral '**look before you leap**'.
  Pick two animals as your main characters and use a similar style to Aesop's fable. Make some notes here then write and illustrate your story on a separate piece of paper.

_____

_____

_____

_____

Taking it further   Read some of Aesop's fables and try to guess the moral. Also look at traditional tales and try to find the moral in them.

Persuasion

Advertisements

- Read the advert below and write down all the examples of persuasive language you can find.

Wonda Pen — The ultimate writing tool!

Have you always wanted neat handwriting?
Have you always wanted a pen that doesn't smudge or leak?
Do you want a pen that can write upside down?
And in water!?

Then you can't afford not to get
the fantastic new
Wonda Pen!

Impress your teachers

State-of-the-art design

Be the envy of your friends

Perfect handwriting every time!

Have you got yours yet? ONLY £5.99 FROM ALL GOOD STATIONERS.

Examples of persuasive language:

_____

_____

_____

_____

_____

_____

Write your own advertisement

- On a separate piece of paper, write your own advert for a fantastic new product that you have invented. Persuade people to buy it with your language.

  Use words and expressions like:

  Unmissable Offer

  Exclusive

What you need to know   How to use persuasive words and phrases; how to make a persuasive argument and express your own point of view; and to be aware of bias (the writer's opinion).

Persuasion can also be used in arguments and letters, when someone wants the reader to share their point of view.

- Read the letter below and answer the questions.

> Dear Editor,
>   I have been forced to write after reading that the ice rink in Garton is going to be knocked down and replaced by yet another supermarket. Surely this can't be true! Why it was only in the last Winter Olympics that our own skating star, Callum Richardson, represented his country, narrowly missing out on a bronze medal.
>   If the ice rink is demolished, where will our future champions come from? There is already very little for young people to do in Garton, without snatching away one of our best-used facilities. Do you really want the young people of Garton to become unfit or to hang round the streets? We should be building more sports facilities instead of more shops.
>   I urge the council to think again. Keep Garton's ice rink!
> Yours faithfully,
>
> S Richardson

- What is the point of view of the person who wrote this letter?

_____

_____

- Find two arguments (reasons) the writer uses to support their point of view.

_____

_____

- In persuasive writing, strong verbs like 'forced', in line 1, are often used. Write down any other strong verbs you can find in the letter.

_____

_____

- On a separate piece of paper, write your own persuasive letter on a subject you feel strongly about. Perhaps there is not enough to do in your town or dogs are making a mess in your park.

- Make a list of all the reasons you can think of to support your argument before you start. Remember to use strong verbs.

Taking it further   Listen to radio adverts. Make up a radio jingle and record it if possible. Play it back and see how it sounds. Persuasive language needs to have a persuasive voice!

Features of poetry

Poets can use poetry to express feelings or set moods by choosing their words carefully.

Here is a poem by Pie Corbett.

A Poem to Be Spoken Silently…

It was so silent that I heard
my thoughts rustle
like leaves in a paper bag…

It was so peaceful that I heard
the trees ease off
their coats of bark…

It was so still that I heard
the paving stones groan
as they muscled for space…

It was so silent that I heard
a page of this book
whisper to its neighbour,
'Look he's peering at us again…'

It was so still that I felt
a raindrop grin
as it tickled the window's pane…

It was so calm that I sensed
a smile crack the face
of a stranger…

It was so quiet that I heard
the morning earth roll over
in its sleep and doze
for five minutes more…

- Now answer these questions about the poem.

- What kind of mood is the poet trying to create?

  _____

- List as many quiet words as you can find in this poem.

  _____   _____   _____

  _____   _____   _____

- Find and write down one simile in this poem.

  _____

- Add another verse to the poem, following the style of the poet.

  It was so _____

  _____

  _____

  _____

What you need to know   There are different types of poems with different feelings. Children need to be able to talk about poems, picking out language, ideas, and saying how it makes them feel. A simile describes something by saying it is like another.

Narrative poems

Some poems tell a story – they are called narrative poems and are often quite long.

Here is part of a narrative poem about a Cup Final football match.

In the tunnel
The teams were ready,
The fans were shouting,
The atmosphere heady.
Standing in line,
With racing hearts,
Twenty-two players,
Waiting to start.
The people cheered,
The noise was deafening,
They took up position,
Nerves were lessening.
The whistle blew,
The game began,
The effort incredible
By every man.

Jolly Joke

Why are football matches always windy?

Because of all the fans!

Thinking about poems

- Think about the poem above and answer these questions.
- What did you like or dislike about the poem?

_____

_____

- What kind of atmosphere is the poet trying to create?

_____

_____

- Find a phrase in the poem that you like and say why you think it is effective.

_____

_____

- Try writing your own narrative poem. Use something that has happened to you or your favourite book or film to give you ideas.

Taking it further   Read poems by different poets and compare them. Talk about how a poem makes you feel and realise that different people may react differently to the same poem. You could read 'The Highwayman' by Alfred Noyes or any of the 'Revolting Rhymes' by Roald Dahl for more examples of narrative poems.

Playscripts

Plays are written in the form of a 'script', which tells the actors what to say and how to say it.

Here is an extract from a play, 'The Web Monster'.

SCENE: a cave with a huge web suspended from the ceiling. Glenn and Chris, with torches and rucksacks, are exploring. They shine the torch on the web and see a huge spider-like creature with three legs.

Glenn: (*whispering*) What is it?

Chris: (   ) I… I… don't know!

Glenn: (*dropping his rucksack*) It looks like a giant spider, but it only has three legs!

Chris: Oh… it's looking at us! Run!

Glenn: (   ) No, let's go and talk to it.

Chris: You must be joking! How do you talk to a monster?

Monster: (   ) Excuse me, it's very rude to talk about someone behind their back. The name's Jason, if you don't mind. (*Extends one of his long, red, hairy arms.*) How do you do?

The words in brackets tell the actor how they should say the lines, or the actions they should do.

- Put a word in each of the brackets to suggest how the line should be spoken.

Props are the equipment actors need in order to act out a scene.

- Write down the props needed for the scene above.

_____

_____

The personalities of the characters can be shown in the words they say and the way they say them.

- Think of words to describe the personalities of:

Glenn _____

Chris _____

Monster _____

What you need to know   How a playscript is set out; that playwrights use words to show us how a character feels; and that directions tell the actors how to say the lines.

Stories can be written in the form of scripts.

Read the story section below. It tells us more about the Web Monster.

In the cave, Jason the Web Monster approached the boys who were shocked more than scared. Glenn bravely spoke first and asked the monster who he was and how he got there. Chris hid behind Glenn, shaking.

Jason explained that he was staying in the cave until his legs grew back after an accident. Then he hoped to return to his home deep inside the earth. Glenn felt suddenly sorry for Jason and asked if there was anything they could do. Chris opened his rucksack and offered the monster a sandwich. Jason politely refused but asked the boys if they could bring him some milk and a blanket, as the nights were cold in the cave.

- Rewrite the above passage as a playscript. Work out the order of the events and what each character might say. Remember to add stage directions to tell the actors how to act and deliver their lines.

SCENE: _____

_____

_____

_____

_____

_____

_____

_____

_____

_____

_____

_____

_____

Taking it further Go and see a play in your local theatre. Read the programme to find out about the characters and an outline of the plot. Write down and act out your own plays; experiment with different voices for the characters.

Instructions

Instructions need to be clear and easy to follow. Read the set of instructions below.

Flapjacks

Recipe information

Serves: 8
Prep time: 10 minutes
Cooking time: 20 minutes

Nutrition

281 calories, 13 g fat (of which saturated fat 6 g), 0·3 g salt, 17 g sugar

Ingredients

100 g unsalted butter
50 g caster sugar
100 g golden syrup
250 g rolled oats
2 teaspoons ground ginger

Method

1 Melt the butter, sugar and syrup together.
2 Stir in the rolled oats and press into a shallow 20 cm square, lightly oiled baking tin.
3 Bake for 18–20 minutes at 190°C, 375°F, gas mark 5 until golden brown, the mixture will still be quite soft.
4 Cool for 15 minutes in the tin and cut into squares or rectangles, lift onto a wire rack to cool completely.

Recipe courtesy of Sainsbury's

- Now answer these questions.

- Why do you think the ingredients have been written before the method?

  _____

  _____

- Why do you think the writer has used numbers for the instructions? What else could they have used?

  _____

  _____

- The words in red are commands called imperatives. They tell us what to do and how to do it. Find four more imperatives in the recipe above.

  _____   _____   _____   _____

- Why might it be a good idea to use pictures or diagrams?

  _____

What you need to know The language used in instructions (commands), and the need to set out instructions clearly in the order that things should be done.

- Write your own set of instructions here.

Here are some ideas to get you started:

how to get to your school from your house; how to juggle;
how to play your favourite game; how to make your favourite pudding.

Checklist:

Are my instructions clear?

Have I used commands?

Have I listed all the things I will need?

Have I set out things in the order they need to be done?

- Get someone to follow your instructions to see if they work!

Jolly Joke

What do jokes and pencils have in common?

They're no good without a point!

Taking it further   Play the directions game. Direct another person across a room by using clear instructions. Or set a treasure hunt for your friends in your house or garden. Leave clear clues with instructions of where to go to find the next one. Have a small prize at the end!

Answers

Page 4
Auto- means self
autobiography, autograph, automobile, automatic

Bi- means two or both
A two wheeled vehicle – bicycle
Helps you to see things at a distance – binoculars
Something that happens every two years – biennial
An aeroplane with two sets of wings – biplane
Able to speak two languages – bilingual

Page 5
Trans- means across or through
transfer, transport, translucent, transform, transplant

Tele- means at a distance
telescope – something to look through
television – something to watch
teleport – Dr Who can do this in his TARDIS
telephone – you can talk to your friends on this
telepathy – the ability to know what someone is thinking

Page 6
Hidden roots
The red part should be circled:
signature, reviewed, helpfulness, selection, untruthful

More root words
Possible answers:
employed, employing, employee, employer, employment, unemployment
fired, firefighter, fireguard, firebreak, firecracker, firearm
foothold, footing, football, footnote, underfoot, footpath
linesman, lined, underline, line-up, liner, linear

Page 7
Follow the pattern
admission   admitted
commission   committed
submission   submitted
omission   omitted
emission   emitted

Experiment with root words
handed, behindhand, handler, handier, handiest, handbook, handbrake, handfeed, handball

Page 8
Find out where
Check your child's spelling.
Possible French words: restaurant, litre, pâté, quiche, déjà vu, cul-de-sac

Page 9
Word meanings
bungalow – a single storey house, word from India.
restaurant – a place where meals are sold and eaten, word from France.
kayak – a canoe, formerly made of animal skin, word from Eskimo (Greenland).
robot – a machine that carries out jobs normally done by humans, word from Czechoslovakia.
anorak – a short weatherproof coat with a hood, word from Eskimo (Greenland).

New words
Check your child's answers.

Page 10
-able or -ible?
portable, horrible, likeable, responsible, washable, terrible
If you take off the ending and you are left with a real word, the ending is likely to -able. If you take off the ending and it doesn't make a real word then the ending is probably -ible.

What is missing?
interest, company, carpet, freedom, poisonous, different, manager, describe, factory

Page 11
Verbs to nouns
hypnotist, hypnotism
tourist, tourism
cyclist
escapist, escapism, escapology

Nouns to verbs
terrorise, terrify
magnetise
vandalise

lengthen
frighten
materialise
horrify
lighten

Page 12
Sentence order
Check your child's answers.

Changing order
Check your child's answers.

Page 13
Most important words
Check your child's answer.

Which words can be left out?
Check your child has crossed out the unnecessary words.
Possible shorter sentences: Steven Sutherland, 23, had returned from six months' holiday in Australia. During the first song, at his first outdoor concert, the guitarist's string broke.

Page 14
Main clauses
an owl hooted; The teacher was pleased; the gnome sat by the pond; Steven cheered

Subordinate clauses
Although it was night-time; when he saw his owner; somewhere in the woods; Up above them

Page 15
Shorter sentences
Possible answers:
The frog croaked, as the rain fell and the pond became full.
The sun shone, so the class were happy because they could play rounders.
Josh likes playing tennis because it is his favourite sport, and he is a good player.
The boy tripped and as he fell over he lost his ice cream.

Building up longer sentences
Check your child's answers.

Page 16
And, but or so
but, but, so, so, and

More connectives
even though/although, even though/although, because, as/because